Superchallenge

GENERAL KNOWLEDGE QUIZ BOOK

From an original format by

John M. Lewis

GW00535794

4

A CHANNEL
FOUR BOOK

BXTREE

To Mum and Dad
(or Kitty and Len if you are not their son).
Thanks for having me.

First published in 1990 by Boxtree Limited

6 8 10 9 7 5

Questions © Boxtree Ltd, 1990

British Library Cataloguing in Publication Data
Anderson, Simon.
    15–1 superchallenge.
    1. Quiz games
    I. Title
    793.73

ISBN 1–85283–135–9

Typeset by Cambrian Typesetters, Frimley, Surrey
Printed and bound in Great Britain by
Cox & Wyman Ltd, Reading, Berkshire
for Boxtree Limited
Broadwall House
21 Broadwall
London SE1 9PL

Jacket design by Head Publications
Questions set by Simon Anderson

Contents

Foreword

What noise annoys an oyster? How many beans make five? Who was that lady I saw you with last night? If you keep watching Fifteen to One I'm sure that you will hear the answers eventually. For those of you who are avid fans of the programme and have watched every show, by the end of the 1990 season you will have heard almost 100,000 questions asked and seen nearly 6,000 contestants answering or attempting to answer them.

They say you need a killer instinct to be a winner on Fifteen to One. I don't know about that, because I haven't got the nerve to take part. But over the past three years we have seen people grimace as they hear their number called by one of their opponents on the semi-circle, and others flinch or scowl as they fall by the wayside and are asked to sit down.

I don't think it pays to be too charitable or appear too vulnerable when taking part, but I believe that good general knowledge combined with a sense of survival and just a smidgen of ruthlessness will stand you in good stead. Each day you can watch fifteen contestants line up to do battle in what has been likened to a Roman arena; so as the saying goes, when in Rome . . .

Have fun trying to answer the questions in the book and watching the quiz on Channel 4, and if you think you have what *you* feel it needs to be a winner on Fifteen to One . . . apply now.

John M. Lewis

Round 1

Simply Hard
Starters

Simple Starters

1. Which Gilbert and Sullivan opera is set in a court of law?

2. In which organ of the body is insulin produced?

3. What name is given to a person who lives west of the river Medway in Kent?

4. What is the family name of the Dukes of Northumberland?

5. What is the national airline of Belgium?

6. Where did the Russians massacre a large number of Polish officers in 1940?

7. What is the Israeli equivalent of the C.I.A.?

8. Where will the 1992 Winter Olympics be held?

9. Who helped to rescue survivors from the wrecked ship *The Forfarshire*, off the Farne Islands in Northumberland?

10. In which century was Joan of Arc burnt at the stake?

11. How is it known that a pope has been elected?

12. For what was the Gobelins workshop in France famous in the seventeenth century?

13. What is the meaning of the Latin phrase *prima facie*?

14. In whose car was Mary Jo Kopechne riding, when she was killed at Chappaquidick in 1969?

15. Name one of the Quarter Days.

Answers on page 78

Wars

1. Who was ruler of Argentina during the Falklands War?

2. What sporting event provoked a war between Honduras and El Salvador in 1969?

3. In which war were the towns of Ladysmith and Mafeking besieged?

4. Which country was in dispute with the UK in the so-called cod war of the 1970s?

5. Which famous battle was fought at Senlac Hill?

6. Which war is depicted in the film *Full Metal Jacket*?

7. In what year did the Spanish Civil War begin?

8. In which century did the Thirty Years' War take place?

9. Which country is known as the cockpit of Europe, because it has so often been a battleground?

10. At which battle in 1746 did the Duke of Cumberland defeat Bonnie Prince Charlie?

11. At which battle was Nelson killed?

12. In which war were the battles of Bunker Hill and Yorktown?

13. At which naval battle were Mark Antony and Cleopatra defeated by Augustus?

14. Which treaty ended the Crimean War?

15. Who was the prime minister of Israel at the time of the Yom Kippur War?

Answers on page 78

Ole Man River

1. Which river, famous for its salmon, forms part of the border between England and Scotland?

2. Which river in South America shares its name with a Womble?

3. By what name is the Hwang Ho better known?

4. In which film was the song *Moon River* featured?

5. Which river does the Ponte Vecchio in Florence span?

6. What is the longest river solely in England?

7. Into which sea does the river Volga flow?

8. On which river is the Kariba Dam?

9. Which well-known Liverpudlian comedian had a top ten hit in the U.K. with a song called *The River*?

10. At which city do the White and Blue Niles meet?

11. Which English river is sometimes known as the Granta?

12. Apart from Vienna and Budapest, through which other capital city does the river Danube flow?

13. What is meant by the phrase crossing the Rubicon?

14. On which river does Washington D.C. stand?

15. Into which bay does the river Ganges flow?

Answers on page 78

Indoor Games

1. What is the lowest number of darts needed to score 501?

2. What is a yarborough?

3. How many pieces does each player have in a game of backgammon?

4. Apart from Colonel Mustard, who are the two other male characters in a game of *Cluedo*?

5. In the crossword of which newspaper did the Normandy invasion code words appear before the invasion?

6. How many dominoes are there in a domino set?

7. What is the name of the Chinese game played with tiles, which became fashionable in Europe and America in the 1920s?

8. What is the equivalent of Mayfair in the American version of *Monopoly*?

9. What is a full house in the game of poker?

10. How much is the letter K worth in *Scrabble*?

11. With which game is the term *en passant* associated?

12. What does a tug on the ear mean in charades?

13. Including the cue ball, how many balls are there on the table at the start of a snooker game?

14. Which number in bingo is called two little ducks?

15. Which piece in chess always remains on the same coloured square?

Answers on page 78

British History

1. Who was the last of the Stuart monarchs?

2. Of which Anglo-Saxon kingdom was Offa the king?

3. Whose reign lasted 44 years?

4. Who summoned the first British "parliament"?

5. In which battle in 1314 did Robert the Bruce defeat Edward II?

6. Which English king formed the *Model Parliament*?

7. In which year was the Act of Union between England and Scotland?

8. What name was given to the group of people who set about breaking up machinery in the early nineteenth century?

9. What name is given to the meeting of Henry VIII and Francis I of France in 1520?

10. In what year was the first Labour government formed in the U.K.?

11. Who was the leader of the Peasants' Revolt of 1381?

12. Which nineteenth century British Foreign Secretary committed suicide with a pair of scissors?

13. At which castle was Mary, Queen of Scots executed?

14. Who was the perpetrator of the Popish Plot?

15. In which year did Britain join the E.E.C.?

Answers on page 79

Little Gems

1. Who played James Bond in the film *Diamonds are Forever*?

2. In which year did Japan launch its attack on the U.S. Pacific Fleet in Pearl Harbor?

3. Who wrote the novel *Coral Island*?

4. Which gemstone is associated with the 40th Wedding Anniversary?

5. What is the name of the world's largest cut diamond?

6. What colour is an amethyst?

7. What is meant by a cultured pearl?

8. Who had a number one hit record in the 1950s with the song *Softly, Softly*?

9. Who played the role of Sapphire in the T.V. series *Sapphire and Steel*?

10. Which city is the centre of the diamond cutting industry in Belgium?

11. Which famous rock star has a daughter called Jade?

12. In which film did Marilyn Monroe sing *Diamonds are a girl's best friend*?

13. Which crown made for Queen Victoria in 1838 contains the ruby owned by the Black Prince and worn by Henry V at Agincourt?

14. In which country is the film *The Emerald Forest* set?

15. In which country is the diamond mining centre of Kimberley?

Answers on page 79

South America

1. Which country was named after a great South American patriot?

2. Which two South American countries have no coastline?

3. What is the longest river in South America?

4. What name is given to the large, treeless plains south of the Amazon?

5. The World Cup football competition has been held 13 times between 1930 and 1986. How many times has it been won by a South American country?

6. At the mouth of which river does Montevideo stand?

7. The film *Kiss of the Spider Woman* was set in a South American jail. Who won a best actor oscar for his performance in the film?

8. What is the official language of Brazil?

9. What is the capital of Ecuador?

10. Which strait separates Chile from Tierra del Fuego?

11. In which country are the Angel Falls, the highest waterfall in the world?

12. Who was overthrown by General Pinochet in 1973?

13. Which is the most populated city in Brazil?

14. With which sport is Maria Bueno associated?

15. Through which three South American countries does the equator run?

Answers on page 79

In Which Year?

In which years did these pairs of events take place?

1. Britain and the U.S.A. were at war. Napoleon won the Battle of Borodino.

2. James II became king of England. Louis XIV revoked the Edict of Nantes.

3. Greece joined the European Community. Ronald Reagan became president of the USA.

4. Edward IV died. Edward V and his brother were murdered in the Tower of London.

5. Revolutions in Europe. Communist Manifesto born.

6. Louis XVI was executed. The Reign of Terror began.

7. John F. Kennedy became president of the USA. Coronation Street started on ITV.

8. Mahatma Gandhi was assassinated. The state of Israel was declared.

9. Mary, Queen of Scots, was executed. Sir Frances Drake destroyed the Spanish fleet at Cadiz.

10. Harold II became king. Harold defeated Norway.

11. Nixon resigned. West Germany won World Cup.

12. The American War of Independence ended. The Montgolfier brothers built their hot-air balloon.

13. Shakespeare was born. Michelangelo died.

14. Prince William born. The SDP founded.

15. Great Fire of London. Newton discovered gravity.

Answers on page 79

Two's Company

1. From which musical does the song *Tea for Two* come?

2. Who is the male star of the ITV situation comedy series *The Two Of Us*?

3. Which pop group had a number one U.K. hit with the song *Two Tribes*?

4. In which years did Sebastian Coe win his two Olympic gold medals for the 1500 metres?

5. Which Italian actress won an oscar for her performance in the film *Two Women*?

6. Who are Valentine and Proteus?

7. Which two politicians won the Nobel Peace Prize in 1973 for their work on peace in Vietnam?

8. What two colours appear on the Polish flag?

9. Which two cities have hosted the Summer Olympic Games twice?

10. With which two countries does Sweden have a land border?

11. Which element has the atomic number 2?

12. Which two rivers meet at the Deutsches Eck near the city of Koblenz?

13. Who were the first two men to walk on the moon?

14. What are the two main ingredients of Angels on Horseback?

15. Of which two animals is a tigon the offspring?

Answers on page 80

In Brief

1. CFCs have a harmful effect on the ozone layer. What do the initials stand for?

2. What abbreviation do the French use for Madame?

3. Which profession is represented by the Union BALPA?

4. What abbreviation is used by the Campaign for Real Ale?

5. What do the letters p.m. stand for?

6. What is SEATO?

7. By what name is Talbot House better known?

8. Which civil honour is denoted by the letters C.H.?

9. Which unit of currency is denoted by the letters D.M.?

10. Where would you find the letters ISBN?

11. Which country's national airline is called KLM?

12. If you saw the letters *pp* over a piece of music, how would it be played?

13. What does N.B. literally stand for?

14. What abbreviation stands for the American Star Wars initiative?

15. What were E.M. Forster's first names?

Answers on page 80

Which Doctor?

1. Which doctor was able to talk to the animals?

2. Who played the title role in *Dr. Finlay's Casebook*?

3. Which famous murderer was the first to be arrested by wireless?

4. Which doctor is president of the Alzheimer's Disease Society and an ex-member of *Beyond the Fringe*?

5. Which two doctors pioneered the first test tube baby?

6. For which constituency is Dr. David Owen M.P.?

7. Which actor played Doctor Who after William Hartnell?

8. Which American group had a top ten hit is 1973 with *Doctor My Eyes*?

9. What does the abbreviation Ph.D stand for?

10. Of which country is Dr. Hastings Banda the head of state?

11. In *Dr. Jekyll and Mr. Hyde* by Robert Louis Stevenson, who commits the murders?

12. Who played the title role in the TV series *Dr. Kildare*?

13. Which doctor was famous for her walks from John O'Groats to Land's End?

14. Who wrote the novels *Doctor in the House* and *Doctor at Large*?

15. Which doctor is famous for his magic bullet?

Answers on page 80

Out Of Africa

1. What is the name of the mountain which overlooks Capetown in South Africa?

2. By what name is the former colony of Southern Rhodesia now known?

3. Which lake is bordered by Kenya, Uganda and Tanzania?

4. What was the name of the secret terrorist society in Kenya in the 1950s?

5. Which sea separates the north-east coast of Africa from Saudi Arabia?

6. What is the capital of Zambia?

7. To which country did Angola once belong?

8. Which country produced the athlete Said Aouita?

9. Who preceded F. W. De Klerk as president of South Africa?

10. Which African desert is the home of the bushmen?

11. What is the connection between a South African archbishop and a ballet dancer's skirt?

12. Which Egyptian-born film actor starred in the films *Lawrence of Arabia* and *Doctor Zhivago*?

13. What is the largest city in Africa?

14. With which African country are both Gordon and Kitchener particularly associated?

15. What is the largest African island?

Three's A Crowd

1. Who were the three heads of state who met at the Yalta Conference?

2. What are the names of the Three Musketeers?

3. Who were the stars of the BBC comedy Series *Three of a Kind*?

4. Who in the Bible were the three men in the burning fiery furnace?

5. What are the three colours of the Dutch flag?

6. Who are the three members of the Benelux customs union?

7. Who were the three sons of Adam and Eve?

8. Who are the three daughters of King Lear?

9. In terms of the British constitution, what are the three estates?

10. What names are usually given to the three magi?

11. What are the names of Chekhov's Three Sisters?

12. Red Rum won the Grand National three times. In which years?

13. What names are given to the three books of Dante's Divine Comedy?

14. Which three countries have borders with Chile?

15. Who were the three poets-laureate before Ted Hughes?

Answers on page 81

Art For Art's Sake

1. In which city is the Uffizi Gallery?

2. What is the popular name of the painting *Arrangement in Grey and Black* by James Whistler?

3. What name is given to a picture made from various materials stuck together?

4. Which pop artist famous for his Campbell's Soup Tins died in 1987?

5. Who painted *The Birth of Venus*?

6. In which gallery is the *Hay Wain* by Constable on show?

7. Whose painting *Impression: Soleil Levant* lent its name to the impressionist school of painting?

8. What is made by applying pigments ground in water to a freshly plastered wall or ceiling?

9. Who painted *The Night Watch*?

10. Which painter inspired Stephen Sondheim to compose the musical *Sunday in the Park with George*?

11. Who painted the portrait of Winston Churchill which was destroyed by his wife?

12. To which British monarch was Van Dyck court painter?

13. Who was Tom Keating?

14. For which Hitchcock film did Salvador Dali design the dream sequence?

15. What nationality was the painter Millais?

Answers on page 81

Radio GaGa

1. In which city is Radio Hereward based?

2. The signature tune of which long running serial is called *Barwick Green*?

3. Who played the character Rambling Syd Rumpo in the comedy series *Round the Horne*?

4. Who succeeded Roy Plomley as presenter of *Desert Island Discs*?

5. Who played the title roles in *The Men from the Ministry*?

6. Which children's programme always included the words *Are you sitting comfortably*?

7. Which two actresses played the part of Mrs Dale in *The Dales*?

8. What was the name of Radio 2 prior to 1967?

9. What was the name of the first pirate radio station?

10. Which programme was introduced by Freddy Grisewood for many years?

11. What was the name of the ventriloquist who appeared in *Educating Archie*?

12. Who was Eccles in *The Goon Show*?

13. Which programme is broadcast every weekday at 5-00 p.m. on Radio 4?

14. What type of programme is Radio 4's *Kaleidoscope*?

15. What town is the radio broadcasting centre of the Netherlands?

Answers on page 81

Uncle Sam

1. How many US states have the word *new* in their name?

2. From which Italian explorer does America take its name?

3. Walter Mondale was the vice-president to which president?

4. Who wrote the plays *A Streetcar Named Desire* and *The Glass Menagerie*?

5. In what year were the oscars first presented?

6. What is a *dime*?

7. What building can be found at number 1600 Pennsylvania Avenue, Washington D.C.?

8. What was the exact date of the Declaration of Independence?

9. What are the two assemblies which make up Congress?

10. What is the name of the warm dry wind which blows over the Rocky Mountains?

11. Which is the oldest and largest national park in the USA?

12. What is the name of the parallel which separates the USA from Canada?

13. What do Americans call *Old Glory*?

14. Which constitutional amendment abolished slavery?

15. Which river forms part of the boundary between Mexico and the USA?

Answers on page 81

All Creatures Great And Small

1. What is a cavy?

2. A herbivore is the term used to describe a plant-eating animal. What word is used for an animal that eats both plants and animals?

3. Which bird has the largest wing span of all?

4. What is unusual about the basenji breed of dog?

5. For what reason were dachshunds originally bred?

6. What type of animal is a basilisk?

7. What animal lives in a drey?

8. What is the biggest type of shark?

9. What type of animal was Rikki Tikki Tavi in Kipling's *Jungle Book*?

10. On the leaves of which plant do silkworms feed?

11. The young of which bird is called a squab?

12. What type of animal was the English artist Stubbs most famous for portraying?

13. What is the largest type of wasp in the UK?

14. Which bird has the scientific name *troglodytes troglodytes*?

15. From which African island do lemurs come?

Answers on page 82

Numbers

1. How many points does a Star of David have?

2. How many muses were there?

3. How many miles are there in 80 kilometres?

4. What do the opposite faces of a standard dice add up to?

5. Which number comes between 20 and 18 on a standard darts board?

6. How many people were killed when the US Space Shuttle Challenger exploded in 1986?

7. What are the two new STD dialling codes for London?

8. How many crowned kings of England have had the name Edward?

9. How many quavers make a minim?

10. In the garden there are 2 badgers, 3 spiders and 2 flamingoes. How many legs are there in total?

11. How many pennies were there in a pre-decimal pound?

12. According to the Paul Hardcastle song, what was the average age of American soldiers in Vietnam?

13. How many operas did Beethoven compose?

14. How many times have Portugal won the Eurovision Song Contest?

15. How many labours did Hercules have to undertake?

Answers on page 82

From Russia With Love

1. What is the literal meaning of the word *Glasnost*?

2. Who was chief of the secret police under Stalin?

3. Who was the last tsar of Russia?

4. What is the capital of Georgia?

5. Into what is the rouble divided?

6. Who wrote the novel *Fathers and Sons*?

7. What is the name of the official Russian Tourist agency?

8. What name is given to the traditional tea-urns heated by charcoal?

9. Which Ivan was known as the Terrible?

10. In which range of mountains is Mount Elbruz, sometimes called Europe's highest peak?

11. How many republics make up the USSR?

12. What is the present name of the city formerly called Stalingrad?

13. Which Russian directed the films *Alexander Nevsky* and *The Battleship Potemkin*?

14. What is G.U.M.?

15. What is the main ingredient in the soup bortsch?

Answers on page 82

Pot Pourri

1. Which Israeli was famous for bending cutlery?

2. What is a quadruped?

3. How many millimetres are there in a metre?

4. What organ stores bile produced in the liver?

5. What is the art of beautiful handwriting called?

6. From which area of France does Camembert cheese come?

7. In which athletic event are the Fosbury Flop, Scissors and Western Roll possible techniques?

8. What does the decibel measure?

9. On what date does St. David's Day fall?

10. The bishop of which city would sign himself by his christian name plus the word Sarum?

11. Between which two places does the annual Oxford and Cambridge Boat Race take place?

12. Which organisation is known as RoSPA?

13. In which year was the Berlin Wall built?

14. What do Nelson, Sammy Davis Junior and the cricketer Colin Milburn have in common?

15. In which country is the Serengeti National Park?

Answers on page 82

World War I

1. Where was the armistice signed after the end of the war?

2. Who commanded the British fleet at the Battle of Jutland?

3. At which battle were tanks first used?

4. Where was Archduke Franz Ferdinand assassinated?

5. Which British liner was sunk by German U-boats on May 7th 1915?

6. What was the name of the treaty between Russia and Germany signed in 1918?

7. How many battles of Ypres were there?

8. Which French hero of World War I was tried for treason after World War II?

9. Which German military leader of World War I became president of Germany in 1925?

10. Where was the German fleet scuttled in 1919?

11. Who became German chief of staff in 1916, directing with Hindenburg, the German war effort?

12. At which battle was poison gas first used?

13. Which peninsula in European Turkey was the scene of unsuccessful landings by the Allies?

14. In which year did the Battle of Verdun start?

15. Which French general dictated the terms of allied victory?

Answers on page 83

Married Bliss

1. Who is the oscar-winning wife of comedian Mel Brooks?

2. What is the name of Mikhail Gorbachev's wife?

3. How many of Henry VIII's wives were executed?

4. Who is married to jazz musician Johnny Dankworth?

5. Which married couple shared the 1903 Nobel Physics Prize?

6. Geoff Durham, who used to be known as the Great Soprendo, has a famous wife. Who is she?

7. In which famous saga does Soames marry Irene?

8. In which year did Prince Charles marry Lady Diana Spencer?

9. What is gamophobia?

10. According to the song, love and marriage go together like what?

11. Who painted *Marriage à la Mode*?

12. What do we call the state of having more than one husband or wife?

13. Whose wives included Britt Ekland, Miranda Quarry and Lynne Frederick?

14. How many times has Elizabeth Taylor been married?

15. Who was Napoleon Bonaparte's second wife?

Answers on page 83

29

Transport

1. Concorde was produced in Bristol and which French city?

2. Which city is served by La Guardia airport?

3. Which country produces Hyundai cars?

4. In which country is there an express train known as the TGV?

5. In which English city is the National Railway Museum situated?

6. Who was the owner of the Belfast-based sports car company which failed in 1982?

7. By what name is the Gravelly Hill Interchange better known?

8. Which city has water buses known as vaporetti?

9. What was the name of the car ferry which sank off the port of Zeebrugge in 1987?

10. In which British city is Temple Meads railway station situated?

11. Who was Minister of Transport when the breathalyser was introduced into Britain in 1967?

12. What is the name of the newest line on the London Underground?

13. Which Scandinavian country changed from driving on the left to the right in 1967?

14. What do the initials P. and O. stand for?

15. What was the name of the airship which crashed near Beauvais in France in 1930?

Answers on page 83

Only Connect

Can you make the connection between the following?

1. a city in Morocco and Tommy Cooper
2. 007 and penicillin
3. a small village and Shakespeare's Prince of Denmark
4. a nineteenth century Italian patriot and a type of biscuit
5. an emu's friend and a Yorkshire city
6. a missile and the film *Rain Man*
7. an alcoholic drink and a type of trap
8. James Stewart's rabbit friend and the circulation of the blood
9. a bespectacled Greek singer and a dog in *Peter Pan*
10. a planet and a Disney dog
11. a new town in Essex and a blonde film star
12. a yellowish-brown coating on metal and a wreckless German pilot
13. a type of dog and an adjective describing part of the Yugoslav coast
14. a town in Staffordshire and a Welsh emblem
15. *Easy Rider* and *On Golden Pond*

Answers on page 83

The Good Book

1. Where was Abraham born?

2. What name is given to the Latin version of the Bible prepared by Jerome in the fourth century?

3. What name is given to the first five books of the Old Testament?

4. Which book of the New Testament starts: "In the beginning was the Word . . ."?

5. Who stole his brother's birthright?

6. Who is the only witch mentioned in the Bible?

7. According to the Gospel of Matthew, who was ordered to carry Jesus' cross?

8. In the parable of the Good Samaritan, which two passed the wounded man without offering help?

9. Where did Noah's Ark come to rest after the Flood?

10. Which biblical character is particularly associated with patience?

11. What relation was John the Baptist to Jesus?

12. What was the occupation of the apostle Matthew before he joined Jesus?

13. In which year was James I's authorised version of the Bible completed?

14. Who was the first to see Jesus after the resurrection?

15. Who was Caiaphas?

Answers on page 84

Pop Goes
The Weasel

1. Which musician played on both sides of the Atlantic at the Live Aid concert?

2. Who were the first Norwegian group to have a number one hit record in the UK?

3. What was the Beatles' biggest selling single?

4. Which members of the Bee Gees are twins?

5. What was the first solo number one in Britain by Diana Ross?

6. With which famous painter was the song *Matchstalk Men and Matchstalk Cats and Dogs* concerned?

7. Of which group were Gary Leeds, Scott Engel and John Maus members?

8. What do the songs *God Save The Queen*, *Relax* and *My Ding A Ling* have in common?

9. Which Irish singer has won the Eurovision Song Contest twice?

10. Who recorded the album *Sticky Fingers*?

11. With whom did Stevie Wonder record the duet *Ebony and Ivory*?

12. Who was Elvis Presley's famous manager?

13. Who was married to Renata Blauel?

14. For which James Bond film did Duran Duran provide the title song?

15. What was George Michael's first solo hit called?

World War II

1. What was the name of the floating harbours used in the D-day landings?

2. Who was controller of Nazi propaganda during World War II?

3. Which country surrendered to the Allies on September 8th 1943?

4. What was the name of the German fortified line set up in opposition to the Maginot line?

5. What name was given to the followers of Brigadier Orde Wingate in Burma?

6. What was the name of the plane which dropped the atom bomb on Hiroshima?

7. What was known as Operation Barbarossa?

8. What event took place on September 2nd, 1945?

9. What is the connection between Omaha, Gold, Utah, Juno and Sword?

10. Which German battleship was scuttled in the River Plate in 1939?

11. Who was the US Chief of Staff between 1939 and 1947?

12. To whom was Rudolf Hess taking his peace proposals, when he parachuted into Scotland in 1941?

13. Which agreement did Hitler violate by crossing the Czech border?

14. When did the Battle of Britain begin?

15. Where was the battleship Royal Oak sunk?

Answers on page 84

Mathematical Problems

1. How many sides has a dodecagon?

2. What is an obtuse angle?

3. What name is given to a quadrilateral with one pair of sides parallel?

4. What is a perfect number?

5. What is an asymptote?

6. How many litres are there in a gallon?

7. What shape has the maximum volume and minimum surface area?

8. Which Scottish mathematician invented logarithms?

9. What is the formula for the circumference of a circle?

10. Which Greek mathematician is considered to be the founder of modern geometry?

11. Which branch of mathematics deals primarily with the relations of sides and angles of a triangle and is much used in astronomy and navigation?

12. In a fraction, the denominator is the lower number, what name is given to the upper number?

13. In a right-angled triangle, what is the longest side called?

14. What are avoirdupois and troy?

15. What is the cube root of 512?

Answers on page 84

Nicknames

1. Which Scottish city is known as the Granite City?

2. Who was The Cheeky Chappie?

3. By what name was the American prisoner Robert Franklin Stroud better known?

4. A British prime minister and a footballer have both been known as Supermac. Can you name them?

5. With which sport was Little Mo associated?

6. Which country is known as the Land of the Rising Sun?

7. Which French revolutionary was known as the Sea-Green Incorruptible?

8. Which American state is the Lone Star State?

9. Who is sometimes known as the Father of English Poetry?

10. Which sportsman is known as the Great White Shark?

11. By what name was the artist Domenicos Theotocopoulous better known?

12. Who is the only English king to have been nicknamed the Great?

13. Which politician's satirical name is Tarzan?

14. By what name was the eleventh century knight Rodrigo Diaz better known?

15. Which football club is nicknamed the Canaries?

Answers on page 85

Royalty

1. Who was the last British Roman Catholic monarch?

2. Which Bavarian king was responsible for the building of Neuschwanstein castle?

3. Who played the king in the 1933 film *The Private Life of Henry VIII*?

4. Which country did the exiled king Constantine rule until 1973?

5. Who was the oldest king to succeed to the British throne?

6. What name is given to the allowance made to the Royal Family by the British government?

7. Who became king of the Belgians in 1951?

8. Which European prince was known as the Navigator?

9. Which British king was married to Alexandra of Denmark?

10. What was the name of Alexander the Great's horse?

11. Which king of France issued the Edict of Nantes and was assassinated by Ravaillac?

12. What was the family name of Richard III?

13. What was the Queen Mother's maiden name?

14. Of which country were the Braganzas the royal family?

15. The wife of Henry II first married Louis VII of France in 1137. Who was she?

Answers on page 85

Feeling Blue

1. Who wrote a play called *The Blue Bird*?

2. In which ballet is there a Bluebird pas de deux?

3. Which rock singer starred in the film *Blue Hawaii*?

4. Which American state is known as the Blue Grass State?

5. Which Spanish-born artist is famous for his blue period?

6. Which pop group had a hit with the song *Blue Monday*?

7. In which Turkish city is the Blue Mosque?

8. In which show was there a character called Bluebottle?

9. Who painted *The Blue Boy*?

10. Which of the home rugby union countries plays in a dark blue shirt?

11. What name is given to the stone mined at Castleton in the Peak District?

12. Why do ships fly the Blue Peter flag?

13. What was the nickname of the man who murdered his wives in the folk tale by Perrault?

14. What name is given to women who affected literary tastes and learning?

15. Which breed of dog has a blue tongue?

Answers on page 85

Eureka!

1. What is the name of the artificial language invented by the Pole Zamenhof?

2. For what invention is Percy Shaw remembered?

3. What nationality was the man who invented the barometer?

4. Which Scottish scientist developed radar?

5. Why should we be thankful to Elisha G. Otis for saving us a lot of effort?

6. In what field were Niépce, Fox Talbot and Carbutt pioneers?

7. Who patented the safety razor in December 1901?

8. Who invented the Spinning Mule in 1779?

9. Which Dutchman is credited with the invention of the telescope?

10. Which invention of 1805 introduced a method of indicating the speed of the wind?

11. Which nation invented paper?

12. Which American politician and scientist who helped to draw up the Declaration of Independence invented the lightning conductor?

13. To which county in England did Marconi transmit his wireless signals from Newfoundland in 1901?

14. What nationality is the man who invented the Rubik Cube?

15. For what invention is Christopher Cockerell famous?

Answers on page 85

Young At Heart

1. In which comic do Lord Snooty and his Pals appear?

2. Which school choir recorded the song *No One Quite Like Grandma*?

3. Which of the seven dwarves wears glasses?

4. What is the name of the lion in *The Wizard of Oz*?

5. What does the acronym UNICEF stand for?

6. Which comic-book hero has the secret identity Peter Parker?

7. What is the name of the comedy duo formed by Jeannette and Ian Tough?

8. Which famous elephant was created by Jean De Brunhoff?

9. Who wrote *The Secret Garden*?

10. Who played the part of Han Solo in the Star Wars films?

11. Who, when asked if he liked children, replied "I do, if they are properly cooked."?

12. Which fictional teddy bear was created by Mary Tourtel?

13. Which toys, which can only be adopted, were invented by Xavier Roberts?

14. What, according to the nursery rhyme, are little boys made of?

15. Who created the character of Biggles?

Answers on page 86

Flowers

1. What colour rose did the Lancastrians adopt in the Wars of the Roses?

2. From where does the name dandelion come?

3. In which of Gilbert and Sullivan's operas does the character Little Buttercup appear?

4. By what name is myosotis more commonly known?

5. Who had a number one hit with the song *Lily the Pink*?

6. With what type of flowers did Gregor Mendel do his genetic experiments?

7. Which plant was featured on the threepenny piece minted between 1937 and 1967?

8. What colour is the flower speedwell?

9. Who played the title role in the film *The Rose*, based on the life story of the rock singer Janis Joplin?

10. *Flowers in the Rain* was the first song to be played on Radio 1. Who recorded it?

11. What is the scientific name of the poisonous plant wolfsbane?

12. What was Benjamin Disraeli's favourite flower?

13. In which part of a flower is the pollen contained?

14. From which country did the tulip originally come?

15. What is the most poisonous plant found in the British Isles?

Answers on page 86

Affairs of State

1. What is the significance of the title Right Honourable before a politician's name?

2. Who was the first female cabinet minister?

3. Who was General Secretary of the T.U.C. before Norman Willis?

4. To what institution are ambassadors to Great Britain accredited?

5. On which day is the budget usually presented?

6. What name is given to the record of parliamentary debates?

7. What is Margaret Thatcher's middle name?

8. What is at number 12, Downing Street?

9. What crisis led to the resignation of Sir Anthony Eden as prime minister?

10. The first referendum in Great Britain was held in 1975. What was its subject?

11. In what year was the voting age reduced to 18?

12. Who said "You've never had it so good"?

13. Whom did Harold Wilson succeed as leader of the Labour Party?

14. If an M.P. applies for the Chiltern Hundreds, what is he doing?

15. In which part of the Palace of Westminster is the Queen's Speech read?

Answers on page 86

On The Box

1. Who played Mrs. Overall in Victoria Wood's spoof soap opera *Acorn Antiques*?

2. In which series does the character of Charlie Hungerford appear?

3. Who is the only original member of the *Coronation Street* cast left in the programme?

4. In which year did Channel 4 begin?

5. What is the ITV teletext service called?

6. Who created the programmes *Brookside*, *Grange Hill* and *Waterfront Beat*?

7. What is the name of Dame Edna Everage's husband?

8. In which programme does *The Woolpack* pub appear?

9. Apart from Dawn French and Jennifer Saunders, who were the two other original *Girls on Top*?

10. Who was Perry Mason's secretary?

11. Who was the first ITN female newsreader?

12. For what type of programme were Hans and Lotte Haas famous?

13. In which American soap opera did the politicians Gerald Ford and Henry Kissinger once appear?

14. With what type of programme were Gerry and Sylvia Anderson particularly associated?

15. Which programme has the theme tune *I Could Be So Good For You*?

Answers on page 86

All At Sea

1. Which sea separates Italy from Sardinia?

2. Who wrote the novel *The Cruel Sea*?

3. In which part of the world are the Kara Sea, the Laptev Sea and the Ross Sea?

4. In which ocean was the Mary Celeste found abandoned in 1872?

5. Where is the Sea of Tranquillity?

6. On which sea are the ports of Baku and Astrakhan?

7. Off the coast of which continent is the Humboldt Current found?

8. What is the name of the deepest part of the Pacific Ocean?

9. Which sea separates Turkey from Greece?

10. Approximately what fraction of the earth's surface is covered by sea?

11. Apart from the USSR, which three other countries have a Black Sea coastline?

12. What is connected to the Caribbean Sea by the Yucatan Strait?

13. Which sea, connected with the Black Sea through the Bosporus and with the Aegean Sea through the Dardanelles, separates Europe from Asia?

14. Which sea is called the Hwang-Hai by the Chinese?

15. What is the name of the sea off the west coast of India?

Answers on page 87

Round 2

Superhard Ones

Getting Harder

1. What does the British Herpetological Society study?

2. In a standard pack of playing cards, which king has only one eye?

3. Who wrote about a village called Cranford?

4. By what name is Annie Mae Bullock better known?

5. Who sculpted *The Burghers of Calais*?

6. To which crop is the boll weevil a particular pest?

7. What is the chemical name for Epsom Salts?

8. Three English football clubs have the word Athletic after their name. Can you name two of them?

9. What type of fruit are Arthur Turner, Discovery and Laxton's Superb?

10. From which Shakespeare play does the line *Brevity is the soul of wit* come?

11. Which religion was founded by Guru Nanak?

12. Which British city was known as Eboracum by the Romans?

13. What is the name of the principal Scottish Order of Chivalry?

14. To which part of the body does the adjective labial apply?

15. Whose fire sometimes plays about the masts of ships during an electric storm?

Answers on page 88

Scientifically Speaking

1. What is the alternative name for deuterium oxide?

2. Which acid has the chemical formula HNO_3?

3. Which element has the chemical symbol K?

4. Who is the 'Father of Modern Chemistry'?

5. In computer jargon, what does COBOL stand for?

6. Which two scientists discovered the structure of DNA?

7. What is the approximate temperature of absolute zero?

8. What name is given to the apparent change in frequency of light or sound, when there is relative motion along a line between the source and the observer?

9. Of what is toxicology the study?

10. What does an anemometer measure?

11. Who wrote *A Brief History of Time*?

12. Who proposed the nuclear model of the atom in 1911?

13. What are the only products of burning pure hydro-carbons?

14. What is the name of the sugar found in milk?

15. What substance is produced by the Haber-Bosch process?

Answers on page 88

Who Said?

1. "Reports of my death are greatly exaggerated"?

2. Which philosopher said "Je pense, donc je suis"?

3. From which play do the lines "All the world's a stage, and all the men and women merely players" come?

4. "Genius is 1% inspiration and 99% perspiration"?

5. From which part of Dante's *Divine Comedy* does the line "Abandon all hope, you who enter here" come?

6. Which comedian was associated with the catchphrase "Before your very eyes"?

7. Of whom did Queen Victoria say: "He speaks to me as if I were a public meeting"?

8. In which of his works did Pope say "A little learning is a dangerous thing"?

9. Which country did Churchill refer to as "A riddle wrapped in a mystery inside an enigma"?

10. "A verbal contract isn't worth the paper it's written on"?

11. From which poem by Coleridge do the lines "Water, water everywhere, Nor any drop to drink" come?

12. Which writer's last words were "More light"?

13. From which film do the words "Frankly, my dear, I don't give a damn" come?

14. Who said: "Publish and be damned"?

15. Which prime minister did Churchill refer to as: "A modest little man with much to be modest about"?

Answers on page 88

Chinese Puzzles

1. What is the monetary unit of China?

2. In which year did China first come under communist rule?

3. What was the name of the uprising of the 1890s, whose aim was to drive foreigners from the country?

4. Who led the Chinese forces against the Japanese in World War II?

5. The nests of which bird are used in bird's nest soup?

6. Which strait separates the Chinese mainland from Taiwan?

7. What is the largest city in China?

8. Why was the Great Wall of China built?

9. Who ruled China from 1644 until 1911?

10. Which are the only two countries in the world bigger in area than China?

11. What was the former name of the city now known as Guangzhou?

12. Who was the president of the first republic of China?

13. In what year did the Long March take place?

14. What is a sampan?

15. Whereabouts in China is the famous terracotta army?

Answers on page 88

Medical Matters

1. At which hospital in Capetown did Dr. Christiaan Barnard perform the first heart transplant in 1967?

2. By what name is the operation for the removal of the uterus known?

3. With which part of the body is the area of rhinology associated?

4. By what name is the disease infectious mononucleosis better known?

5. Who is Louise Brown?

6. What is the name of the clinic in Budapest, famous for its treatment of cerebral palsy?

7. Which bone in the body is known as the clavicle?

8. Which part of the body is affected by bursitis?

9. For what reason do people take beta blockers?

10. For what reason would a doctor use an otoscope?

11. Why would a patient be given a diuretic drug?

12. In childbirth, what is a breech delivery?

13. Who was the doctor who pioneered the role of women in the medical profession?

14. What is an embolism?

15. What do the initials M.E. stand for?

Answers on page 89

Geography

1. What is moraine?

2. What name is given to a narrow strip of land connecting two greater land masses?

3. What name is given to the part of the earth between 23°27′S and 23°27′N?

4. What is a tsunami?

5. In which country is the Atacama Desert?

6. What is the name of the wind which blows down the Adriatic from Central Europe?

7. Of which British moor is Dunkery Beacon the highest point?

8. What number on the Beaufort Scale denotes a hurricane?

9. What is a mesa?

10. In which direction must one cross the International Date Line in order to gain a day?

11. What name is given to the hot dry wind which blows from the Sahara?

12. Which sixteenth century Flemish geographer is particularly noted for his map projection?

13. How much of an iceberg appears above the surface?

14. What is magma?

15. Which is the next largest ocean after the Pacific and the Atlantic?

Answers on page 89

Famous Buildings

1. Whose official residence is the Palais Schaumburg?

2. In which English county are Chatsworth House and Repton School?

3. Which cathedral has the tallest spire in the world?

4. What is unusual about the door of 10, Downing Street?

5. What was the name of Elvis Presley's house?

6. For which king was Fontainebleau built?

7. What does the word *kremlin* mean?

8. Where is the Royal Mint situated?

9. Who had the Taj Mahal built for his wife?

10. In which city is the Topkapi Palace?

11. With whom is the house Sutton Place associated?

12. What is the name of the famous opera house in Milan?

13. Where in London is the Conservative Party Headquarters?

14. On which river does Balmoral Castle stand?

15. What is the correct name for the Houses of Parliament?

Answers on page 89

A Mixed Bag

1. Which Latin poet wrote 12 books about Aeneas?

2. Of which country is Baghdad the capital?

3. What is the name of the valley in West Germany, where the bones of prehistoric man were discovered in the nineteenth century?

4. What is the name of the small triangular bone at the base of the spinal column in man?

5. What is the name of the swamp region of southern Florida, notable for its wildlife?

6. Who wrote *Thus Spake Zarathustra*?

7. The name of which Venetian painter is used to describe bright golden auburn hair?

8. What is the correct name for the making of patterns by inlaying different coloured pieces of wood?

9. In which city is the Sikh golden temple situated?

10. Which unpopular childhood pudding is made from the root of the cassava plant?

11. What was the name of the Dorset farm labourers transported for forming a union?

12. What is the last letter of the Greek alphabet?

13. Who became king of England, Scotland and Ireland in 1660?

14. What name is given to an irresistible tendency to steal what one could afford to buy?

15. What was the surname of the writers Edith, Osbert and Sacheverell?

Answers on page 89

Europe

1. Which treaty created the European Economic Community in 1957?

2. Of the five UN Secretary Generals so far, how many originated from Europe?

3. Which country has the forint as its unit of currency?

4. Not including the USSR, which is the largest country in Europe?

5. What name is given to the French speaking inhabitants of Belgium?

6. Which country has the cockerel as its symbol?

7. In which West German city is the famous Reeperbahn street?

8. Which of the Scandinavian countries has the largest population of Lapps?

9. The flag of Luxembourg is identical to which other European country?

10. Of which modern European country is Moravia now a part?

11. Which maritime European country has the shortest coastline?

12. What do the French call the Straits of Dover?

13. Of which country is La Brabançonne the anthem?

14. What are the four official languages of Switzerland?

15. What was the name of the treaty of 1929 which recognized the sovereignty of the Vatican?

Answers on page 90

Religion

1. What is the highest caste of Hinduism?

2. What name is given to the flight of Mohammed from Mecca to Medina in A.D. 622?

3. Who was the founder of the Christian Science movement?

4. From which country did Zoroastrianism originate?

5. What name is given to the mohammedan crier who proclaims the hours of prayer from a minaret?

6. With which country is the Coptic Church particularly associated?

7. What is the date of Epiphany?

8. Which religious sect publishes *The Watch Tower*?

9. How many theses did Luther nail to the door of Wittenberg Church?

10. What position did John Paul II hold before becoming pope?

11. What is the last word in the New Testament?

12. In which country is Shintoism the chief faith?

13. According to Buddhism, what is the perfect state towards which everyone should strive?

14. By what name is the Chinese philosopher K'ung Fu-Tzu better known?

15. In which calendar are there months called Tishri, Adar and Tebet?

Answers on page 90

The Silver Screen

1. Which actress has won the greatest number of oscars?

2. Who composed the music to the film *Chariots of Fire*?

3. In which Marilyn Monroe film did the wind blow up her skirt?

4. Of which of his films did Alfred Hitchcock make a second version?

5. Which comedian's career was ruined because of a scandal over a starlet's death?

6. From which film did the song *When the Going Gets Tough* by Billy Ocean come?

7. What is the French equivalent of an oscar called?

8. Which was Robert Redford's first film as a director?

9. What is the motto of MGM films?

10. How many versions of *The Thirty-Nine Steps* have been made?

11. On which island was *Zorba the Greek* set?

12. Which film had as its slogan: 'In space no one can hear you scream'?

13. On which Japanese film was *The Magnificent Seven* based?

14. How may films did Richard Burton make with Elizabeth Taylor?

15. Who directed the film *Casablanca*?

Answers on page 90

Voyages of Discovery

1. Where in Africa did Stanley find Livingstone?

2. Which Portuguese navigator made the first voyage from Europe to India round the Cape of Good Hope?

3. Which French underwater explorer invented the aqualung?

4. What feat did the explorers Robert Burke and William Wills achieve in 1861?

5. In which city was Christopher Columbus born?

6. After which Danish explorer is the strait between Alaska and Russia named?

7. Who crossed the Atlantic in a leather boat in 1977?

8. Who was the first man to fly over the North Pole?

9. Who played Scott in *Scott of the Antarctic*?

10. Who was the first American woman in space?

11. Which Spaniard explored Peru in the 1530s and founded the city of Lima as the new capital?

12. Who sailed round the world on *Lively Lady*?

13. With which area of the world is the explorer Speke particularly associated?

14. What was the name of Thor Heyerdahl's papyrus reed boat?

15. Which Norseman colonised Greenland?

Answers on page 90

My Word!

1. What is a polyandrist?

2. What is the opposite of to estivate?

3. What word is used to describe a person who compiles dictionaries?

4. What is an ampersand?

5. From which language does the word marmalade originally come?

6. In Australian slang, what does the word *dinkum* mean?

7. In Cockney rhyming slang, what is sometimes called a *jam jar*?

8. What is unusual about the vowels in the words *abstemiously* and *facetiously*?

9. Which American president gave his name to the teddy bear?

10. What does the Latin phrase *caveat emptor* mean?

11. From which film does the word *supercalifragilistic-expialidocious* come?

12. Of what is the triskaidekaphobe frightened?

13. What is an antonym?

14. What name is given to a word formed from the initial letters of other words e.g. NATO, ERNIE etc.

15. What is the medical name for lock-jaw?

Answers on page 91

Our World

1. Of which country was Vytautis Landsbergis recently elected president?

2. For what do the initials ANC stand?

3. By what name was Sellafield nuclear plant previously known?

4. Which Nobel Prize-winning Russian physicist and human rights activist died in 1989?

5. Who was the leader of East Germany, who resigned at the end of 1989?

6. Who took over from Kenneth Baker as Secretary of State for Education?

7. Of which country is Kim Il Sung the autocratic leader?

8. Who succeeded Rajiv Gandhi as prime minister of India?

9. In which country is the town of Timisoara?

10. In which country is the war-torn state of Tigre?

11. Which state of the USSR has been involved in hostilities with its neighbour, Armenia?

12. In which Commonwealth island was a coup staged in 1987?

13. Which major engineering project floated its shares in December 1987?

14. Who succeeded President Zia as leader of Pakistan?

15. Who is the leader of the extreme right-wing in France?

Answers on page 91　　　59

Myths and Legends

1. Who was the Greek goddess of victory?

2. How did Hercules cleanse the Augean stables?

3. Who was the Muse of Love Poetry?

4. Who were the twin sons of Zeus and Leda?

5. Which mythical animal had the head of an eagle and the body of a lion?

6. In Norse mythology, what is the name of the home of the gods?

7. What name was given to the drink of the Greek gods?

8. Of which island was Ulysses king?

9. Who was the Egyptian Sun god?

10. What was the name of the boatman who ferried people to the underworld?

11. Who or what was Cerberus?

12. How was Prometheus punished for stealing fire from heaven?

13. What name is given to the monsters dwelling in the forests of Scandinavia?

14. What, besides hope, was in Pandora's box?

15. The Greek god of wine was Dionysus. Who was his Roman equivalent?

Answers on page 91

Classical Music

1. Of which composer were the Esterhazy family patrons?

2. Who was the great rival of Mozart who claimed to have poisoned him?

3. What does the term *rallentando* on a piece of music mean?

4. Which of Beethoven's symphonies was originally dedicated to Napoleon?

5. By what name is Schubert's *Piano Quintet in A* known?

6. In which opera do the characters of Godfrey, Elsa and Telramund appear?

7. Who wrote the play on which Rossini's *Barber of Seville* is based?

8. What is the name given to a composition for a solo instrument in combination with an orchestra?

9. Which town in West Germany is famous for its Wagner festivals?

10. Who composed *The Brandenburg Concertos*?

11. Which famous conductor was the son of a drug millionaire?

12. What instrument is played by Vladimir Horowitz?

13. Who composed the anthem *Zadok the Priest*, played at every coronation in the UK for the last 300 years?

14. Which composer's life was featured in the film *The Music Lovers*?

15. Which composer wrote *The War Requiem*?

Answers on page 91

Sporting Chance

1. Which sport is played by the Pittsburgh Steelers and the Washington Redskins?

2. Which was the first country to win the football World Cup in 1930?

3. Who defeated Bjorn Borg in the 1981 Wimbledon Men's Tennis final?

4. How many times have the Summer Olympics been held in the United Kingdom?

5. At which racecourse are the 1,000 and 2,000 guineas run?

6. In polo, into what are the periods of play divided?

7. In which capital city is the Bislett stadium?

8. What type of gymnastic exercise is a sukahara?

9. In which sport would you be required to swim, shoot, run, ride and fence?

10. In which sport is the Swaythling Cup presented?

11. What nationality was the heavyweight boxing champion Ingemar Johansson?

12. Which village in Hampshire is particularly associated with the development of cricket?

13. Where is the Dutch motor racing grand prix held?

14. What is the nickname of the South African Rugby Union team?

15. With which sport are Roland Matthes and Kornelia Ender associated?

Answers on page 92

Lakes

1. In which country are the lakes Tegernsee, Schliersee and Chiemsee?

2. The French call this lake *Lac Léman*. By what name do we know it?

3. Erie, Michigan, Ontario and Superior are four of the Great Lakes. What is the fifth?

4. What is the largest lake in the United Kingdom?

5. On which lake is the city of Kampala situated?

6. In which country is Lake Balaton?

7. What is the deepest lake in the United Kingdom?

8. In which Italian lake is the island of Isola Bella?

9. The Bitter Lakes are part of which canal system?

10. In which Scandinavian country are lakes Vänern and Vättern?

11. Who wrote about the lake isle of Innisfree?

12. Who were known as the Lake Poets?

13. On which lake was Donald Campbell killed, while trying to break the water speed record?

14. The Germans call it *Bodensee*. What do we call it?

15. Which lake on the border between Peru and Bolivia is situated at an altitude of over 12,500 feet?

Answers on page 92

Food and Drink

1. What does the UHT stand for on a packet of UHT milk?

2. What are ricotta, tilsiter and bleu de Bresse?

3. Who is the resident wine expert on BBC 2's *Food and Drink* programme?

4. What would the term *Lyonnaise* indicate on a menu?

5. What does the word *brut* indicate on a champagne bottle?

6. From which fruit is the liqueur calvados made?

7. With which country do you associate enchiladas and tortillas?

8. Which town in north-west England is famous for its mint cake?

9. From what type of pastry are profiteroles made?

10. Name two of the five main vegetables used in the making of ratatouille.

11. Ghee is often used in Indian cookery. What is it?

12. How did spam get its name?

13. Apart from rum, what are the other two main ingredients of a pina colada?

14. What is a John Dory?

15. What name is given to the pudding made of beaten egg yolks and Marsala wine?

Answers on page 92

Climb Every Mountain

1. Which two countries have a range of mountains called the Sierra Nevada?

2. In which country are the Drakensberg Mountains?

3. Which mountain in Greece was sacred to Apollo?

4. Which face of the Eiger is the hardest to climb?

5. What nationalities were the first two men to conquer Everest?

6. In which country is Mount Ararat?

7. What is the highest mountain in the western hemisphere?

8. Who was the first man to climb the Matterhorn?

9. By what name is Mont Cervin better known?

10. How many of the ten highest peaks in the UK are in Scotland?

11. What range of mountains forms part of the border between East and West Germany?

12. In which American state is Mount McKinley?

13. Which German writer produced a novel called *The Magic Mountain*?

14. What do Cotopaxi, Popocatapetl, Mauna Loa and Stromboli have in common?

15. What name is shared by a Scottish island and a range of French–Swiss mountains?

Answers on page 92

Round 3

Super-challenging Ones

The Hard Ones

1. Which British newspaper produced the first colour magazine in 1962?

2. In ballet, what is an entrechat?

3. Of which country is bushkazi the national game?

4. In what year did the Lisbon earthquake take place?

5. What nationality was the first non-American and non-Russian man to go into space?

6. In heraldry, what colour is gules?

7. Who was the founder of the Bauhaus school of arts and crafts?

8. The flag of which country is not rectangular in shape?

9. What substance was used by South American Indians to poison the tips of their arrows?

10. What is the unit of currency of Finland?

11. In which city is the oldest Stock Exchange in the world?

12. Which treaty ended the Thirty Years' War?

13. From which country do stamps with the word *Shqiperia* on them come?

14. Which British football club plays at Tannadice Park?

15. What relation was Kublai Khan to Genghis Khan?

Answers on page 93

Down Under

1. What is the highest point in Australia?

2. What is the title of the man who represents Her Majesty the Queen in Australia?

3. Which actor played the part of Scott Robinson in *Neighbours* before Jason Donovan?

4. What is the capital of Queensland?

5. Where was originally known as Van Diemen's Land?

6. Which Australian racing driver won the World Drivers' Championship in 1980?

7. Which Australian actress won a BAFTA award for *My Brilliant Career*?

8. Which Australian writer won the Nobel Prize for Literature in 1973?

9. Who is the lead singer of the pop group INXS?

10. How many players are there on an Australian Rules football side?

11. Which Australian artist painted *Themes from the Career of Ned Kelly*?

12. How many stars are there on the Australian flag?

13. What is the gulf in the north of Australia which is bordered by Cape York peninsula on the east side?

14. What is the name of the egg-laying mammal peculiar to Australia?

15. What do the initials QANTAS stand for?

Answers on page 93

Stargazing

1. What is peculiar about the direction of a comet's tail?

2. Who was the first Astronomer Royal?

3. Which planet has moons called Ariel, Miranda, Oberon and Titania?

4. Which planet was discovered by Clyde Tombaugh in 1930?

5. What name is given to the point in a planet's orbit at which it is nearest to the sun?

6. What name is given to the belts of radiation surrounding the Earth?

7. Which astronomer was imprisoned for teaching that the Earth was not the centre of the universe?

8. Which is the nearest galaxy to the Milky Way?

9. Which theory of the origin of the universe was first advanced by Georges Lemaitre?

10. Which is the brightest star in the sky?

11. What name is given to the thin gaseous atmosphere of the Sun, visible as a pearly glow at a total eclipse?

12. How far is the Earth from the Sun?

13. With which animal is the constellation Cetus associated?

14. Of what are Saturn's rings made up?

15. What nationality was the astronomer Tycho Brahe?

Answers on page 93

Crimewatch

1. Where was Benigno Aquino assassinated in 1983?

2. What is a polygraph?

3. What was the name of the prostitute involved in the Jeffery Archer libel case?

4. Which former 400 metre runner was jailed for dealing in steroids?

5. Which British historian authenticated the forged Hitler diaries sold to the German magazine *Stern*?

6. What were Bonnie and Clyde's surnames?

7. What name is given to the Chinese secret criminal societies based in Hong Kong?

8. Who was executed for kidnapping Charles Lindbergh's son?

9. In which country do the Yakuza operate?

10. Who was the British ambassador to Uruguay who was kidnapped by Tupamaros Guerillas in 1971?

11. Why was Tory M.P. Keith Best forced to resign his seat?

12. In which city is the prison Sing Sing?

13. At which hotel was Margaret Thatcher staying when it was blown up by the I.R.A.?

14. By what name was the multiple murderer David Berkowitz sometimes known?

15. A security warehouse at Heathrow was robbed of £25 million pounds in 1984. By what name is the robbery known?

Answers on page 93

Island Hopping

1. Which Caribbean island was invaded by the United States in 1983?

2. To which group of Greek islands do Patmos, Kos and Rhodes belong?

3. Excluding Australia, which is the world's largest island?

4. What is the name of the island shared by Haiti and the Dominican Republic?

5. What is the predominant religion of Sri Lanka?

6. What is the capital of Sardinia?

7. On which of the Japanese islands is Tokyo situated?

8. Of which island group was Queen Salote once ruler?

9. By what name is the former Anglo-French condominium New Hebrides now known?

10. Which island in the Netherlands Antilles gives its name to a liqueur?

11. What is the name of the highest peak on the Isle of Man?

12. The parliament of which island country is known as the Althing?

13. By what name is the Indonesian island of Celebes sometimes known?

14. On which island is the city of Copenhagen?

15. Which of the four main Balearic Islands is closest to mainland Spain?

Answers on page 94

Testing Teasers

1. With which sport are Beryl Burton and Bernard Hinault associated?

2. By what name is the playwright Jean Baptiste Poquelin better known?

3. What is meant by the right of primogeniture?

4. In what field was Sir Mortimer Wheeler prominent?

5. Who was the founder of the experimental school Summerhill?

6. Where in India did the worst-ever chemical accident take place in 1984?

7. What is a pangolin?

8. Who was William Tell's main enemy?

9. What name is given to the disease which involves compulsive eating?

10. Who was the French founder of the philosophy called positivism?

11. Of what is cryogenics the study?

12. For what was Boris Onischenko infamous in 1976?

13. Which island has a parliament called The Court of Chief Pleas?

14. Where in Algeria were the headquarters of the French Foreign Legion?

15. What is a morganatic marriage?

Answers on page 94

Heads of State

1. Which Cuban dictator was overthrown by Fidel Castro in January 1959?

2. What is the family name of Prince Rainier of Monaco?

3. Who was president of the United States of America during World War I?

4. Which Egyptian president was assassinated by rebel soldiers while reviewing a military parade?

5. Who succeeded Gustav Husak as President of Czechoslovakia?

6. Of which country was Vigdis Finnbogadottir the first female president?

7. What was the name of the repressive police force employed by the Duvaliers in Haiti?

8. Who is the King of Nepal?

9. By whom was Indira Gandhi assassinated?

10. Who led Albania from the Second World War until his death in April 1985?

11. The President of France is one of the joint heads of state of Andorra. Who is the other?

12. Who abdicated as Queen of the Netherlands in 1980 in favour of her daughter?

13. For how long is the French President elected?

14. The head of state of which country is known as An Uachtaran?

15. Who succeeded Hirohito as emperor of Japan?

Answers on page 94

Cities

1. The second largest city in Armenia suffered greatly in the recent earthquake. What is its name?

2. What is the more familiar name for the capital city Krung Thep?

3. Which architect designed many of the buildings in Brasilia?

4. What is the largest city inside the Arctic Circle?

5. What city was the capital of Australia before Canberra?

6. Which is the largest French speaking city after Paris?

7. What is the name of the port of Athens?

8. On which river does Kiev stand?

9. In which country is the ancient city of Machu Picchu?

10. Of which country is Paramaribo the capital?

11. Which British city has the most canals?

12. What is the alternative name for the German city of Aachen?

13. In which capital city is the Shway Dagon Pagoda?

14. In which city is the famous Manneken-Pis statue?

15. Which city is the capital of the state of California?

Answers on page 94

Literature

1. Which Spanish poet and playwright was killed by Fascists in 1936?

2. Whose chronicles did Shakespeare often use as background for his historical plays?

3. Whose autobiography is *Chronicles of Wasted Time*?

4. *Justine*, *Balthazar* and *Mountolive* are three of the books of the Alexandria Quartet by Lawrence Durrell. What is the fourth?

5. During which riots is *Barnaby Rudge* by Charles Dickens set?

6. In which novel is Raskolnikov the central character?

7. What is the name of the flying island in *Gulliver's Travels*?

8. In which of Jane Austen's novels is Fanny Price the heroine?

9. Who created the detective Sexton Blake?

10. Who wrote the 1985 Booker Prize winning novel, *The Bone People*?

11. In which of Sheridan's plays do Lydia Languish and Captain Absolute appear?

12. Who translated *The Rubaiyat of Omar Khayyam* into English?

13. In memory of whom did Shelley write *Adonais*?

14. Who wrote the novel *Gone with the Wind*?

15. Which film, other than *Carbaret*, was based on Christopher Isherwood's *Goodbye to Berlin*?

Answers on page 95

Science

1. Of what is palaeontology the study?

2. What is measured in candelas?

3. What name is given to the phenomenon, whereby a substance on heating changes directly from solid to gas without first melting to a liquid?

4. In computing jargon, how many bits are there in a byte?

5. What is the main metal extracted from bauxite?

6. Whose law states that at constant temperature the volume of a gas is inversely proportional to the pressure exerted on it?

7. What name is given to the force that acts outwardly on an object moving in a circular path?:

8. What name is given to sound waves beyond the range of human hearing?

9. What is meant by an ecosystem?

10. Which scientist experimented with the effect of electricity on frogs' legs?

11. What does the acronym laser stand for?

12. In chemical reactions, catalysts are often used. What are they?

13. Which acid is present in vinegar?

14. What is the common name for ethylene glycol?

15. Which is the softest mineral?

Answers on page 95

Answers Round 1: Simply Hard

SIMPLE STARTERS

1. *Trial by Jury*.
2. The pancreas.
3. Kentish Man.
4. Percy.
5. Sabena.
6. Katyn.
7. The Mossad.
8. Albertville, France.
9. Grace Darling.
10. The fifteenth.
11. White smoke comes out of a Vatican chimney.
12. Tapestry making.
13. At first sight.
14. Senator Edward Kennedy's.
15. Lady Day, Midsummer Day, Michaelmas, Christmas.

OLE MAN RIVER

1. The Tweed.
2. The Orinoco.
3. The Yellow River.
4. *Breakfast at Tiffany's*.
5. The Arno.
6. The Thames.
7. The Caspian Sea.
8. The Zambezi.
9. Ken Dodd.
10. Khartoum.
11. The Cam.
12. Belgrade.
13. Being committed to an enterprise, with no turning back.
14. The Potomac.
15. The Bay of Bengal.

WARS

1. General Galtieri.
2. A football match.
3. The Boer War.
4. Iceland.
5. The Battle of Hastings.
6. The Vietnam War.
7. 1936.
8. The seventeenth century (1618–1648).
9. Belgium.
10. Culloden.
11. Trafalgar.
12. The American War of Independence.
13. Actium.
14. The Treaty of Paris.
15. Golda Meir.

INDOOR GAMES

1. Nine.
2. A whist or bridge hand with no card above a nine.
3. Fifteen.
4. Professor Plum and the Reverend Green.
5. *The Daily Telegraph*.
6. Twenty-eight.
7. Mah Jong.
8. Boardwalk.
9. A hand containing three of a kind and a pair.
10. Five.
11. Chess.
12. That the word sounds like another word.
13. Twenty-two.
14. Twenty-two.
15. The bishop.

BRITISH HISTORY

1. Anne.
2. Mercia.
3. Elizabeth I.
4. Simon de Montfort.
5. Bannockburn.
6. Edward I.
7. 1707.
8. Luddites.
9. *The Field of the Cloth of Gold.*
10. 1924.
11. Wat Tyler.
12. Lord Castlereagh.
13. Fotheringay, Northamptonshire.
14. Titus Oates.
15. 1973.

LITTLE GEMS

1. Sean Connery.
2. 1941.
3. R. M. Ballantyne.
4. The ruby.
5. The Cullinan Stone.
6. Violet.
7. A pearl which has been induced by introducing an object into the oyster.
8. Ruby Murray.
9. Joanna Lumley.
10. Antwerp.
11. Mick Jagger.
12. *Gentlemen Prefer Blondes.*
13. The Imperial State Crown.
14. Brazil.
15. South Africa.

SOUTH AMERICA

1. Bolivia.
2. Bolivia and Paraguay.
3. The Amazon.
4. The pampas.
5. Seven (Uruguay: 1930, 1950; Brazil; 1958, 1962, 1970; Argentina: 1978, 1986).
6. The Rio de la Plata (River Plate).
7. William Hurt.
8. Portuguese.
9. Quito.
10. The Straits of Magellan.
11. Venezuela.
12. Salvador Allende.
13. Sao Paulo.
14. Tennis.
15. Ecuador, Colombia and Brazil

IN WHICH YEAR

1. 1812.
2. 1685.
3. 1981.
4. 1483.
5. 1848.
6. 1793.
7. 1960.
8. 1948.
9. 1587.
10. 1066.
11. 1974.
12. 1783.
13. 1564.
14. 1982.
15. 1666.

TWO'S COMPANY

1. *No, No, Nanette.*
2. Nicholas Lyndhurst.
3. Frankie Goes To Hollywood.
4. 1980 and 1984.
5. Sophia Loren.
6. The Two Gentlemen of Verona.
7. Henry Kissinger and Le Duc Tho.
8. White and red.
9. Paris: 1900 and 1924; London: 1908 and 1948.
10. Norway and Finland.
11. Helium.
12. The Rhine and the Moselle.
13. Neil Armstrong and Buzz Aldrin.
14. Oysters and bacon.
15. A tiger and a lioness.

WHICH DOCTOR?

1. Doctor Dolittle.
2. Bill Simpson.
3. Doctor Crippen.
4. Jonathan Miller.
5. Edwards and Steptoe.
6. Plymouth Devonport.
7. Patrick Troughton.
8. The Jackson Five.
9. Doctor of Philosophy.
10. Malawi.
11. Mr. Hyde.
12. Richard Chamberlain.
13. Doctor Barbara Moore.
14. Richard Gordon.
15. Paul Ehrlich.

IN BRIEF

1. Chlorofluorocarbons.
2. Mme.
3. Airline pilots (British Airline Pilots Association).
4. CAMRA.
5. Post meridiem.
6. The South-East Asia Treaty Organization.
7. Toc H.
8. Companion of Honour.
9. The Deutschmark.
10. In a book (International Standard Book Number).
11. The Netherlands.
12. Very softly (pianissimo).
13. Nota Bene (note well).
14. S.D.I. (Strategic Defence Initiative).
15. Edward Morgan.

OUT OF AFRICA

1. The Table Mountain.
2. Zimbabwe.
3. Victoria.
4. The Mau Mau.
5. The Red Sea.
6. Lusaka.
7. Portugal.
8. Morocco.
9. P. W. Botha.
10. The Kalahari.
11. Tutu.
12. Omar Sharif.
13. Cairo.
14. The Sudan.
15. Madagascar.

THREE'S A CROWD

1. Churchill, Stalin and Roosevelt.
2. Athos, Porthos and Aramis.
3. Tracey Ullman; Lenny Henry; David Copperfield.
4. Shadrach, Mesach and Abednego.
5. Red, white and blue.
6. Belgium, the Netherlands and Luxembourg.
7. Cain, Abel and Seth.
8. Goneril, Regan and Cordelia.
9. The Lords Spiritual, Temporal and the Commons.
10. Caspar; Melchior; Balthazar.
11. Masha, Olga and Irina.
12. 1973, 1974 and 1977.
13. *Inferno*, *Purgatorio*, *Paradiso*.
14. Argentina, Bolivia and Peru.
15. Betjeman, Day-Lewis and Masefield.

ART FOR ART'S SAKE

1. Florence.
2. *Whistler's Mother*.
3. A collage.
4. Andy Warhol.
5. Sandro Botticelli.
6. The National Gallery
7. Monet.
8. A fresco.
9. Rembrandt.
10. Seurat.
11. Graham Sutherland.
12. Charles I.
13. A forger of paintings.
14. *Spellbound*.
15. British.

RADIO GAGA

1. **Peterborough**.
2. *The Archers*.
3. Kenneth Williams.
4. Michael Parkinson.
5. Wilfred Hyde-White and Richard Murdoch.
6. *Listen With Mother*.
7. Ellis Powell and Jessie Matthews.
8. The Light programme.
9. Radio Caroline.
10. *Any Questions*.
11. Peter Brough.
12. Spike Milligan.
13. P.M.
14. An arts magazine.
15. Hilversum.

UNCLE SAM

1. Four (New Hampshire, New Jersey, New Mexico, New York).
2. Amerigo Vespucci.
3. Jimmy Carter.
4. Tennessee Williams.
5. 1929.
6. 10 cents.
7. The White House.
8. July 4th 1776.
9. The Senate and the House of Representatives.
10. The Chinook.
11. Yellowstone.
12. The 39th.
13. The US flag.
14. The 13th.
15. The Rio Grande.

ALL CREATURES GREAT AND SMALL

1. Another name for a guinea pig.
2. An omnivore.
3. The albatross.
4. It cannot bark.
5. For badger hunting.
6. A lizard.
7. A squirrel.
8. The Whale Shark.
9. A mongoose.
10. Mulberry.
11. A pigeon.
12. Horses.
13. The hornet.
14. The wren.
15. Madagascar.

FROM RUSSIA WITH LOVE

1. Openness.
2. Beria.
3. Nicholas II.
4. Tbilisi.
5. Kopeks.
6. Turgenev.
7. Intourist.
8. Samovars.
9. Ivan IV.
10. The Caucasus.
11. Fifteen.
12. Volgograd.
13. Sergei Eisenstein.
14. A large shop in Moscow.
15. Beetroot.

NUMBERS

1. Six.
2. Nine.
3. Fifty.
4. Seven.
5. One.
6. Seven.
7. Inner London: 071
   Outer London: 081.
8. Six (Edward V and Edward VIII were not crowned).
9. Four.
10. Thirty-six.
11. 240.
12. Nineteen.
13. One.
14. They have never won it.
15. Twelve.

POT POURRI

1. Uri Geller.
2. A four-footed animal.
3. One thousand.
4. The gall bladder.
5. Calligraphy.
6. Normandy.
7. The high jump.
8. Sound intensity.
9. March 1st.
10. Salisbury.
11. Putney and Mortlake.
12. The Royal Society for the Prevention of Accidents.
13. 1961.
14. Only one eye.
15. Tanzania.

WORLD WAR I

1. In a railway carriage at Compiègne.
2. John Jellicoe.
3. The Somme, 1916
4. Sarajevo.
5. The Lusitania.
6. Brest-Litovsk.
7. Three.
8. Pétain.
9. Paul von Hindenburg.
10. Scapa Flow.
11. Erich Ludendorff.
12. Ypres, 1915.
13. Gallipoli.
14. 1916.
15. Ferdinand Foch.

MARRIED BLISS

1. Anne Bancroft.
2. Raisa.
3. Two: Anne Boleyn and Catherine Howard.
4. Cleo Laine.
5. The Curies.
6. Victoria Wood.
7. *The Forsyte Saga*.
8. 1981.
9. Fear of marriage.
10. A horse and carriage.
11. William Hogarth.
12. Polygamy.
13. Peter Sellers.
14. Seven.
15. Marie Louise of Austria.

TRANSPORT

1. Toulouse.
2. New York.
3. South Korea.
4. France.
5. York.
6. John De Lorean.
7. Spaghetti Junction.
8. Venice.
9. The Herald of Free Enterprise.
10. Bristol.
11. Barbara Castle.
12. The Jubilee line.
13. Sweden.
14. Peninsular and Oriental.
15. R101.

ONLY CONNECT

1. Fez.
2. Fleming.
3. Hamlet.
4. Garibaldi.
5. Hull.
6. Cruise.
7. Gin.
8. Harvey.
9. Nana.
10. Pluto.
11. Harlow.
12. Rust.
13. Dalmatian.
14. Leek.
15. Fonda.

THE GOOD BOOK

1. Ur.
2. The Vulgate.
3. The Pentateuch.
4. The Gospel according to John.
5. Jacob.
6. The Witch of Endor.
7. Simon of Cyrene.
8. A priest and a Levite.
9. On Mount Ararat.
10. Job.
11. Cousin.
12. Tax-collector.
13. 1611.
14. Mary Magdalene.
15. The high priest of the Jews to whom Jesus was first taken after his arrest.

POP GOES THE WEASEL

1. Phil Collins.
2. A-ha.
3. *I Wanna Hold Your Hand*.
4. Maurice and Robin Gibb.
5. *I'm Still Waiting*.
6. L. S. Lowry.
7. The Walker Brothers.
8. They were all banned by the BBC.
9. Johnny Logan.
10. The Rolling Stones.
11. Paul McCartney.
12. Colonel Tom Parker.
13. Elton John.
14. *A View to a Kill*.
15. *Careless Whisper*.

WORLD WAR II

1. Mulberry Harbours.
2. Goebbels.
3. Italy.
4. The Siegfried Line.
5. The Chindits.
6. Enola Gay.
7. The German invasion of the USSR.
8. VJ Day (Victory over Japan).
9. They were the code-names for the Normandy landing beaches.
10. *The Graf Spee*.
11. George C. Marshall.
12. The Duke of Hamilton and Lord Simon.
13. The Munich agreement.
14. July 1940.
15. Scapa Flow.

MATHEMATICAL PROBLEMS

1. Twelve.
2. An angle of more than 90 degrees.
3. A trapezium.
4. A number which is equal to the sum of all the numbers by which it is divisible.
5. A line that approaches a curve, but never touches it.
6. 4.5.
7. A sphere.
8. John Napier.
9. $2 \pi r$ (r = radius).
10. Euclid.
11. Trigonometry.
12. The numerator.
13. The hypotenuse.
14. Systems of weights.
15. Eight.

NICKNAMES

1. Aberdeen.
2. Max Miller.
3. The Birdman of Alcatraz.
4. Harold Macmillan and Malcolm Macdonald.
5. Tennis (Maureen Connolly).
6. Japan.
7. Robespierre.
8. Texas.
9. Chaucer.
10. Greg Norman.
11. El Greco.
12. Alfred.
13. Michael Heseltine.
14. El Cid.
15. Norwich.

ROYALTY

1. James II.
2. Ludwig II.
3. Charles Laughton.
4. Greece.
5. William IV, aged 64.
6. The Civil List.
7. Baudouin.
8. Henry of Portugal.
9. Edward VII.
10. Bucephalus.
11. Henry IV.
12. Plantagenet.
13. Bowes-Lyon.
14. Portugal.
15. Eleanor of Aquitaine.

FEELING BLUE

1. Maurice Maeterlinck.
2. *The Sleeping Beauty.*
3. Elvis Presley.
4. Kentucky.
5. Picasso.
6. New Order
7. Istanbul.
8. The Goons.
9. Gainsborough.
10. Scotland.
11. Blue John.
12. As a signal that they are about to sail.
13. Bluebeard.
14. Blue stockings.
15. A chow.

EUREKA!

1. Esperanto.
2. Cat's-eyes.
3. Italian (Torricelli).
4. Sir Robert Watson-Watt.
5. He invented the first mechanical lift.
6. Photography.
7. King C. Gillette.
8. Samuel Crompton.
9. Hans Lippershey.
10. The Beaufort Scale.
11. The Chinese.
12. Benjamin Franklin.
13. Cornwall.
14. Hungarian.
15. The hovercraft.

YOUNG AT HEART

1. *The Beano*.
2. St. Winifred's School Choir.
3. Doc.
4. Zeke.
5. United Nations International Children's Emergency Fund.
6. Spider-Man.
7. The Krankies.
8. Babar.
9. Frances Hodgson Burnett.
10. Harrison Ford.
11. W. C. Fields.
12. Rupert.
13. The Cabbage Patch Kids.
14. Slugs and snails and puppy dogs' tails.
15. Captain W. E. Johns.

FLOWERS

1. Red.
2. From the French *Dent de Lion* – Lion's tooth.
3. *HMS Pinafore*.
4. Forget-me-not.
5. Scaffold.
6. Sweet Pea.
7. The thrift.
8. Blue.
9. Bette Midler.
10. The Move.
11. Aconite.
12. The primrose.
13. The anther.
14. Turkey.
15. Deadly nightshade.

AFFAIRS OF STATE

1. It means he is a Privy Councillor.
2. Margaret Bondfield.
3. Len Murray.
4. The Court of St. James.
5. Tuesday.
6. Hansard.
7. Hilda.
8. The Whip's Office.
9. Suez.
10. The Common Market.
11. 1969.
12. Harold Macmillan.
13. Hugh Gaitskell.
14. Resigning.
15. The House of Lords.

ON THE BOX

1. Julie Walters.
2. *Bergerac*.
3. Kenneth Barlow (William Roache).
4. 1982.
5. Oracle.
6. Phil Redmond.
7. Norm.
8. *Emmerdale*.
9. Ruby Wax and Tracey Ullman.
10. Della Street.
11. Anna Ford.
12. Underwater exploring.
13. *Dynasty*.
14. Puppet programmes.
15. *Minder*.

ALL AT SEA

1. The Tyrrhenian Sea.
2. Nicholas Montsarrat.
3. The Arctic.
4. The Atlantic.
5. On the Moon.
6. The Caspian Sea.
7. South America.
8. The Marianas Trench.
9. The Aegean Sea.
10. Five eighths.
11. Turkey, Bulgaria and Romania.
12. The Gulf of Mexico.
13. The Sea of Marmara.
14. The Yellow Sea.
15. The Arabian Sea.

Round 2: Superhard Ones

GETTING HARDER

1. Reptiles and amphibians.
2. The king of diamonds.
3. Mrs. Gaskell.
4. Tina Turner.
5. Rodin.
6. Cotton.
7. Magnesium Sulphate.
8. Oldham, Charlton and Wigan.
9. Apples.
10. *Hamlet*.
11. Sikhism.
12. York.
13. The Order of the Thistle.
14. The lips.
15. St. Elmo's.

SCIENTIFICALLY SPEAKING

1. Heavy water.
2. Nitric acid.
3. Potassium.
4. Antoine Lavoisier.
5. Common Business Oriented Language.
6. Crick and Watson.
7. −273 degrees C.
8. The Doppler effect.
9. Poisons.
10. Wind speed.
11. Stephen Hawking.
12. Rutherford.
13. Water and carbon dioxide.
14. Lactose.
15. Ammonia.

WHO SAID?

1. Mark Twain.
2. René Descartes.
3. *As You Like It*.
4. Thomas Edison.
5. *The Inferno*.
6. Arthur Askey.
7. Gladstone.
8. *An Essay on Criticism*.
9. The Soviet Union.
10. Samuel Goldwyn.
11. *The Ancient Mariner*.
12. Goethe.
13. *Gone With The Wind*.
14. The Duke of Wellington.
15. Attlee.

CHINESE PUZZLES

1. The yuan.
2. 1949.
3. The Boxer Rebellion.
4. Chiang Kai-Shek.
5. The swift.
6. The Formosa Strait.
7. Shanghai.
8. As a defence against nomadic raiders.
9. The Manchus.
10. The USSR and Canada.
11. Canton.
12. Sun Yat Sen.
13. 1934.
14. A flat-bottomed boat.
15. Xian.

MEDICAL MATTERS

1. Groote Schuur.
2. A hysterectomy.
3. The nose.
4. Glandular fever.
5. The first test-tube baby.
6. The Peto Institute.
7. The collar-bone.
8. The joints.
9. To lower their blood pressure.
10. To look down your ear.
11. To increase the flow of urine.
12. The delivery of the baby bottom first, instead of head first.
13. Elizabeth Garrett Anderson.
14. The blockage of an artery by an air bubble or blood clot.
15. Myalgic Encephalomyelitis.

FAMOUS BUILDINGS

1. The Chancellor of the Federal Republic of Germany.
2. Derbyshire.
3. Ulm Cathedral.
4. It cannot be opened from the outside.
5. Graceland.
6. Francis I.
7. Citadel.
8. Llantrisant, Wales.
9. Shah Jehan.
10. Istanbul.
11. Paul Getty.
12. La Scala.
13. Smith Square.
14. The Dee.
15. The Palace of Westminster.

GEOGRAPHY

1. Debris carried down and deposited by a glacier.
2. An isthmus.
3. The Tropics.
4. A tidal wave under the sea's surface, caused by an earthquake.
5. Chile.
6. The Bora.
7. Exmoor.
8. Twelve.
9. A high rocky tableland with precipitous sides.
10. From west to east.
11. The Harmattan.
12. Gerardus Mercator.
13. About one ninth.
14. Molten rock which becomes igneous rock when it solidifies.
15. The Indian Ocean.

A MIXED BAG

1. Vergil.
2. Iraq.
3. Neanderthal.
4. The coccyx.
5. The Everglades.
6. Nietzsche.
7. Titian.
8. Marquetry.
9. Amritsar.
10. Tapioca.
11. The Tolpuddle Martyrs.
12. Omega.
13. Charles II.
14. Kleptomania.
15. Sitwell.

EUROPE

1. The Treaty of Rome.
2. Three: Trygve Lie (Norway), Dag Hammarskjold (Sweden), Kurt Waldheim (Austria).
3. Hungary.
4. France.
5. Walloons.
6. Portugal.
7. Hamburg.
8. Norway.
9. The Netherlands.
10. Czechoslovakia.
11. Monaco.
12. Pas de Calais.
13. Belgium.
14. French, German, Italian, Romansch.
15. The Lateran Treaty.

RELIGION

1. Brahman.
2. The hegira.
3. Mary Baker Eddy.
4. Persia.
5. The muezzin.
6. Egypt.
7. January 6th.
8. The Jehovah's Witnesses.
9. 95.
10. Archbishop of Cracow.
11. Amen.
12. Japan.
13. Nirvana.
14. Confucius.
15. The Jewish calendar.

THE SILVER SCREEN

1. Katharine Hepburn.
2. Vangelis.
3. *The Seven Year Itch.*
4. *The Man Who Knew Too Much.*
5. Fatty Arbuckle.
6. *The Jewel of the Nile.*
7. A césar.
8. *Ordinary People.*
9. *Ars Gratia Artis* (Art for the sake of Art).
10. Three: 1935, 1959, 1978.
11. Crete.
12. *Alien.*
13. *The Seven Samurai.*
14. Eleven.
15. Michael Curtiz.

VOYAGES OF DISCOVERY

1. Ujiji.
2. Vasco Da Gama.
3. Jacques Cousteau.
4. They crossed Australia from the south to the north.
5. Genoa.
6. Vitus Bering.
7. Tim Severin.
8. Admiral Richard Byrd.
9. John Mills.
10. Sally Ride.
11. Francisco Pizarro.
12. Sir Alec Rose.
13. Africa (The Nile).
14. Ra.
15. Leif Ericsson.

MY WORD!

1. A woman with more than one husband.
2. To hibernate.
3. A lexicographer.
4. A symbol used instead of the word *and*.
5. Portuguese.
6. Honest.
7. A car.
8. They feature in the order a, e, i, o, u.
9. Theodore Roosevelt.
10. Let the buyer beware.
11. Mary Poppins.
12. The number 13.
13. A word of opposite meaning to another.
14. An acronym.
15. Tetanus.

OUR WORLD

1. Lithuania.
2. African National Congress.
3. Windscale.
4. Andrei Sakharov.
5. Erich Honecker.
6. John Macgregor.
7. North Korea.
8. V. P. Singh.
9. Romania.
10. Ethiopia.
11. Azerbaijan.
12. Fiji.
13. The Channel Tunnel (Eurotunnel).
14. Benazir Bhutto.
15. Jean-Marie Le Pen.

MYTHS AND LEGENDS

1. Nike.
2. By diverting rivers through them.
3. Erato.
4. Castor and Pollux.
5. The griffin.
6. Asgard.
7. Nectar.
8. Ithaca.
9. Ra.
10. Charon.
11. A three-headed dog, guarding the gate to Hell.
12. He was chained to a mountain, while vultures ate his liver.
13. Trolls.
14. All the ills of human life.
15. Bacchus.

CLASSICAL MUSIC

1. Haydn.
2. Antonio Salieri.
3. Becoming slower.
4. The Third: *Eroica*.
5. The Trout Quintet.
6. *Lohengrin*.
7. Beaumarchais.
8. A concerto.
9. Bayreuth.
10. J. S. Bach.
11. Sir Thomas Beecham.
12. The piano.
13. Handel.
14. Tchaikovsky.
15. Benjamin Britten.

SPORTING CHANCE

1. American football.
2. Uruguay.
3. John McEnroe.
4. Twice: 1908 and 1948.
5. Newmarket.
6. Chukkas.
7. Oslo.
8. A vault.
9. The modern pentathlon.
10. Table tennis.
11. Swedish.
12. Hambledon.
13. Zandvoort.
14. The Springboks.
15. Swimming.

LAKES

1. West Germany.
2. Lake Geneva.
3. Huron.
4. Lough Neagh, Northern Ireland.
5. Victoria.
6. Hungary.
7. Loch Morar, Scotland.
8. Maggiore.
9. The Suez Canal.
10. Sweden.
11. W. B. Yeats.
12. Wordsworth, Southey and Coleridge.
13. Coniston.
14. Lake Constance.
15. Titicaca.

FOOD AND DRINK

1. Ultra High Temperature.
2. Types of cheese.
3. Jill Goolden.
4. With onions.
5. Very dry.
6. Apples.
7. Mexico.
8. Kendal.
9. Choux.
10. Aubergines, courgettes, peppers, tomatoes, onions.
11. Clarified butter.
12. It is a shortened version of spiced ham.
13. Pineapple juice and coconut milk.
14. A type of fish.
15. Zabaglione.

CLIMB EVERY MOUNTAIN

1. Spain and the United States of America.
2. South Africa.
3. Parnassus.
4. The north face.
5. New Zealander (Edmund Hillary), Nepalese (Sherpa Tenzing Norgay).
6. Turkey.
7. Aconcagua.
8. Edward Whymper.
9. The Matterhorn.
10. All of them.
11. The Harz Mountains.
12. Alaska.
13. Thomas Mann.
14. They are all volcanoes.
15. Jura.

Round 3: Super-challenging Ones

THE HARD ONES

1. *The Sunday Times*.
2. A leap striking the heels together.
3. Afghanistan.
4. 1755.
5. Czech.
6. Red.
7. Walter Gropius.
8. Nepal.
9. Curare.
10. The markka.
11. Amsterdam.
12. The Treaty of Westphalia.
13. Albania.
14. Dundee United.
15. Grandson.

DOWN UNDER

1. Mount Kosciusko.
2. The governor-general.
3. Darius Perkins.
4. Brisbane.
5. Tasmania.
6. Alan Jones.
7. Judy Davis.
8. Patrick White.
9. Michael Hutchence.
10. Eighteen.
11. Sidney Nolan.
12. Six.
13. The Gulf of Carpentaria.
14. The platypus.
15. Queensland and Northern Territory Aerial Services.

STARGAZING

1. It always points away from the sun.
2. John Flamsteed.
3. Uranus.
4. Pluto.
5. The perihelion.
6. The Van Allen Belts.
7. Galileo.
8. Andromeda.
9. The big bang theory.
10. Sirius.
11. The corona.
12. 93 million miles.
13. The whale.
14. Ice and rock.
15. Danish.

CRIMEWATCH

1. At Manila airport, the Philippines.
2. A lie detector.
3. Monica Coghlan.
4. David Jenkins.
5. Lord Dacre (Hugh Trevor-Roper).
6. Bonnie Parker and Clyde Barrow.
7. The triads.
8. Bruno Hauptmann.
9. Japan.
10. Geoffrey Jackson.
11. He had made multiple share applications to British Telecom.
12. New York.
13. *The Grand Hotel*, Brighton.
14. Son of Sam.
15. The Brinks Mat Robbery.

ISLAND HOPPING

1. Grenada.
2. The Dodecanese.
3. Greenland.
4. Hispaniola.
5. Buddhism.
6. Cagliari.
7. Honshu.
8. Tonga.
9. Vanuatu.
10. Curaçao.
11. Snaefell.
12. Iceland.
13. Sulawesi.
14. Zealand.
15. Ibiza.

HEADS OF STATE

1. Fulgencio Batista.
2. Grimaldi.
3. Woodrow Wilson.
4. Anwar Al-Sadat.
5. Vaclav Havel.
6. Iceland.
7. The Tonton Macoutes.
8. Birendra.
9. Two Sikh members of her bodyguard.
10. Enver Hoxha.
11. The Bishop of Urgel (from Spain).
12. Juliana.
13. Seven.
14. The Republic of Ireland.
15. Akihito.

TESTING TEASERS

1. Cycling.
2. Molière.
3. The right of succession belonging to the first son.
4. Archaeology.
5. A. S. Neill.
6. Bhopal.
7. A scaly anteater.
8. Gessler.
9. Bulimia.
10. Auguste Comte.
11. Very low temperatures.
12. For cheating in the fencing section of the Modern Pentathlon at the Montreal Olympics in 1976.
13. Sark.
14. Sidi Ben Abbas.
15. One between a man of high rank and a commoner, where the latter and her offspring have no claims of succession.

CITIES

1. Leninakan.
2. Bangkok.
3. Oscar Niemeyer.
4. Murmansk.
5. Melbourne.
6. Montreal.
7. Piraeus.
8. The Dnieper.
9. Peru.
10. Surinam.
11. Birmingham.
12. Aix-la-Chapelle.
13. Rangoon.
14. Brussels.
15. Sacramento.

LITERATURE

1. Federico Garcia Lorca.
2. Holinshed's Chronicles.
3. Malcolm Muggeridge.
4. *Clea*.
5. The Gordon Riots.
6. *Crime and Punishment by* Fyodor Dostoyevsky.
7. Laputa.
8. *Mansfield Park*.
9. Harry Blyth.
10. Keri Hulme.
11. *The Rivals*.
12. Edward Fitzgerald.
13. John Keats.
14. Margaret Mitchell.
15. *I Am A Camera*.

SCIENCE

1. Fossilised animals and plants.
2. Luminous intensity.
3. Sublimation.
4. Eight.
5. Aluminium.
6. Boyle's Law.
7. The centrifugal force.
8. Ultrasonic waves.
9. A community of organisms and the habitat in which they live.
10. Luigi Galvani.
11. Light amplification by stimulated emission of radiation.
12. Substances which speed up a reaction, but are not changed by it.
13. Acetic acid.
14. Antifreeze.
15. Talc.